The balloon

A playscript
adapted from a story by
Roderick Hunt

by Jacquie Buttriss and Ann Callander

Characters

Narrator

Wilf

Wilma

Mrs May

This play has four speaking parts so that it can be read aloud in small groups. Sound effects can be added by children when they are familiar with the playscript but they have not been written in.

Narrator The children were outside.

Wilma Look at the hot air balloon.

Mrs May I have a secret.

Wilf What is it?

Mrs May I want to go in a balloon.

Mrs May It's time to watch television.

Wilma Look at the television.

Narrator The television went wrong.

Mrs May Oh no!

Wilf Look at the photocopier.

Mrs May Oh blow!

Wilf Look at the computer.

Mrs May Oh bother!

Narrator Wilf and Wilma came home.

Wilma Look at this letter.

Wilf The school wants money.
I have an idea.

Mrs May I like Wilf's idea.

Wilma It's a good idea.

Narrator Everyone bought tickets.

Mrs May bought lots of tickets.

Mrs May I want to go in the balloon.

Wilma Mrs May won the prize.

Mrs May I won a ride in the balloon.

Wilf Hooray!

Narrator Mrs May went up in the balloon.

Wilma Hooray!

Mrs May It's wonderful.

Narrator She looked down at the park.

Mrs May I will take a picture.

Wilma The school made lots of money.

Wilf We bought lots of things.

Narrator Mrs May was pleased.
She gave Wilf a present.

Wilf Thank you.

The end

Printed in Hong Kong